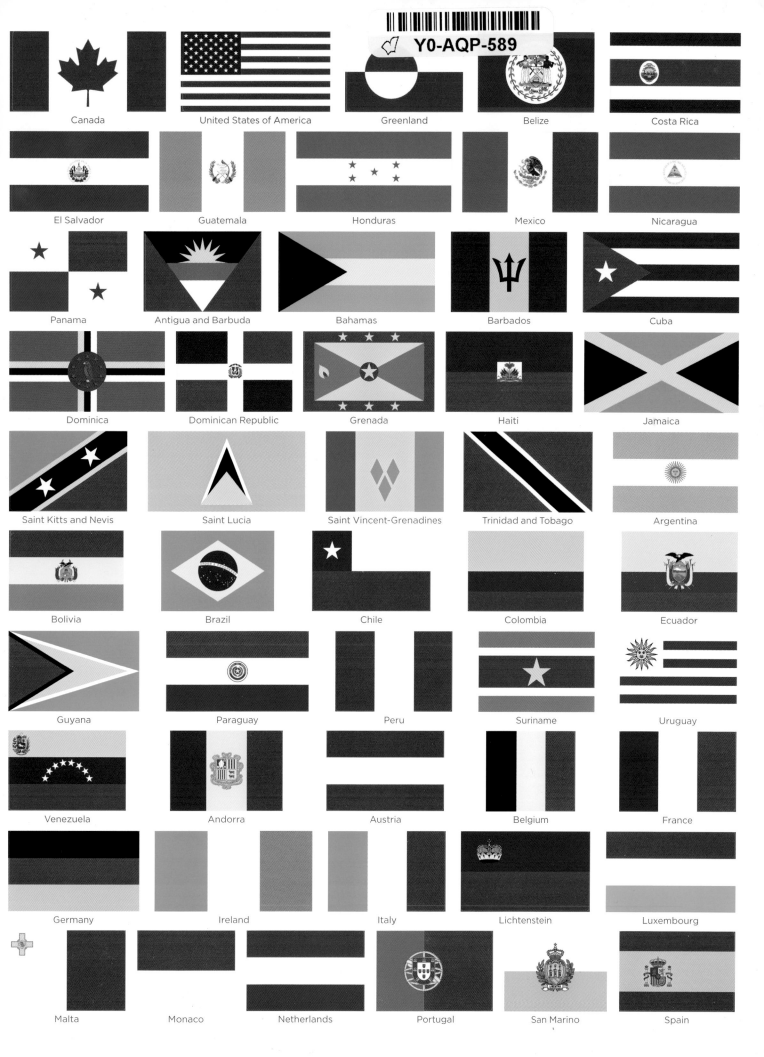

Canada	United States of America	Greenland	Belize	Costa Rica
El Salvador	Guatemala	Honduras	Mexico	Nicaragua
Panama	Antigua and Barbuda	Bahamas	Barbados	Cuba
Dominica	Dominican Republic	Grenada	Haiti	Jamaica
Saint Kitts and Nevis	Saint Lucia	Saint Vincent-Grenadines	Trinidad and Tobago	Argentina
Bolivia	Brazil	Chile	Colombia	Ecuador
Guyana	Paraguay	Peru	Suriname	Uruguay
Venezuela	Andorra	Austria	Belgium	France
Germany	Ireland	Italy	Lichtenstein	Luxembourg
Malta	Monaco	Netherlands	Portugal	San Marino	Spain

Y0-AQP-589

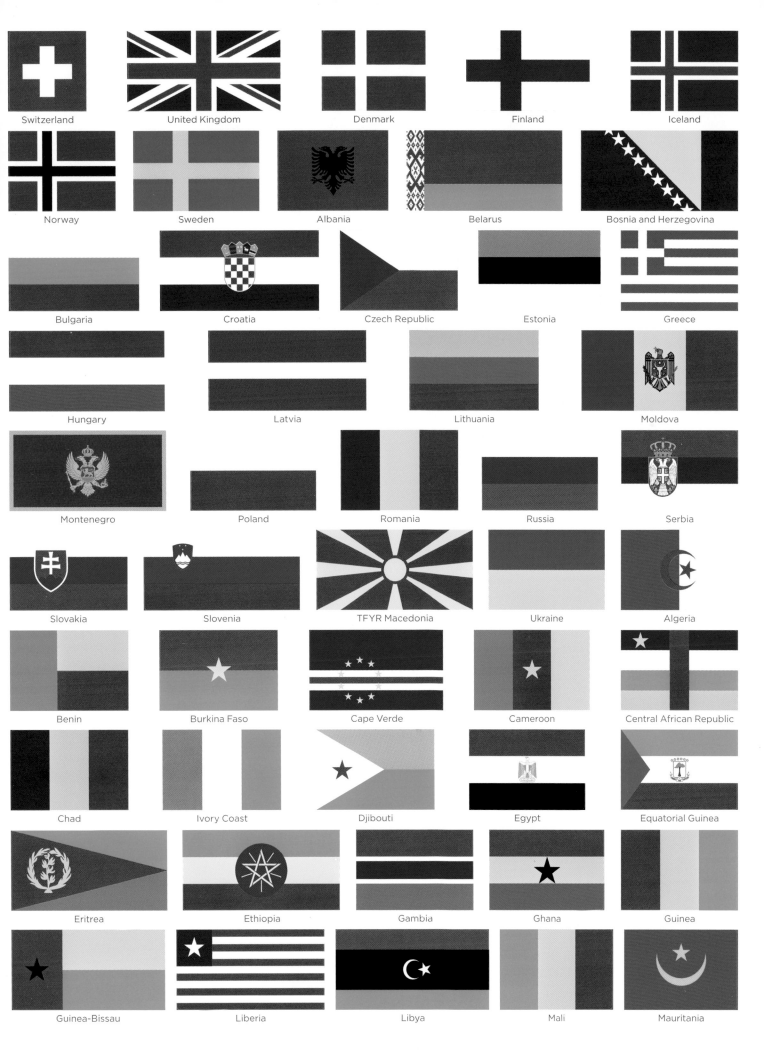

Switzerland

United Kingdom

Denmark

Finland

Iceland

Norway

Sweden

Albania

Belarus

Bosnia and Herzegovina

Bulgaria

Croatia

Czech Republic

Estonia

Greece

Hungary

Latvia

Lithuania

Moldova

Montenegro

Poland

Romania

Russia

Serbia

Slovakia

Slovenia

TFYR Macedonia

Ukraine

Algeria

Benin

Burkina Faso

Cape Verde

Cameroon

Central African Republic

Chad

Ivory Coast

Djibouti

Egypt

Equatorial Guinea

Eritrea

Ethiopia

Gambia

Ghana

Guinea

Guinea-Bissau

Liberia

Libya

Mali

Mauritania

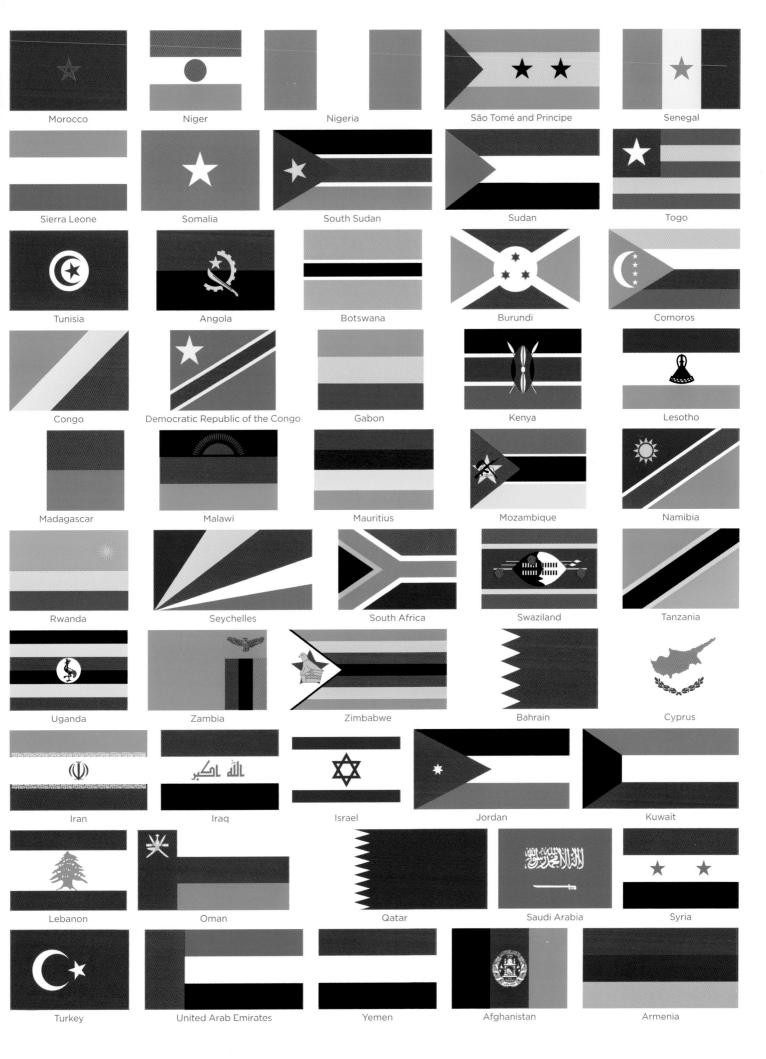

Morocco

Niger

Nigeria

São Tomé and Principe

Senegal

Sierra Leone

Somalia

South Sudan

Sudan

Togo

Tunisia

Angola

Botswana

Burundi

Comoros

Congo

Democratic Republic of the Congo

Gabon

Kenya

Lesotho

Madagascar

Malawi

Mauritius

Mozambique

Namibia

Rwanda

Seychelles

South Africa

Swaziland

Tanzania

Uganda

Zambia

Zimbabwe

Bahrain

Cyprus

Iran

Iraq

Israel

Jordan

Kuwait

Lebanon

Oman

Qatar

Saudi Arabia

Syria

Turkey

United Arab Emirates

Yemen

Afghanistan

Armenia

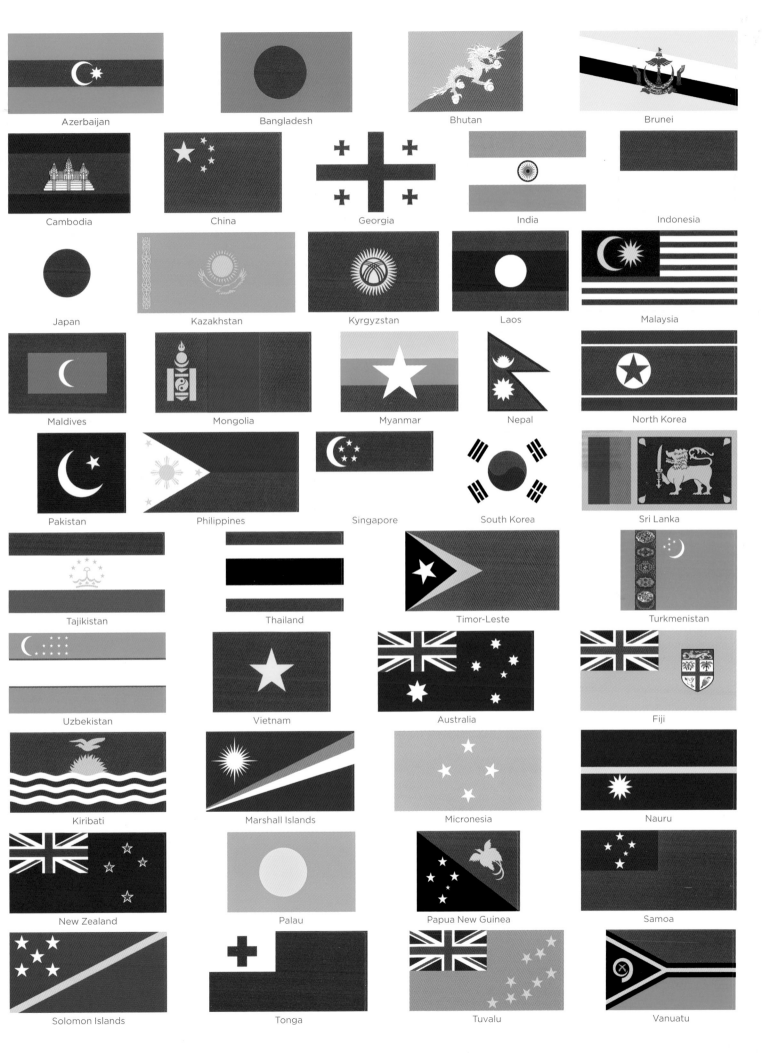

Azerbaijan

Bangladesh

Bhutan

Brunei

Cambodia

China

Georgia

India

Indonesia

Japan

Kazakhstan

Kyrgyzstan

Laos

Malaysia

Maldives

Mongolia

Myanmar

Nepal

North Korea

Pakistan

Philippines

Singapore

South Korea

Sri Lanka

Tajikistan

Thailand

Timor-Leste

Turkmenistan

Uzbekistan

Vietnam

Australia

Fiji

Kiribati

Marshall Islands

Micronesia

Nauru

New Zealand

Palau

Papua New Guinea

Samoa

Solomon Islands

Tonga

Tuvalu

Vanuatu

FLAGS
OF THE WORLD

STICKER BOOK

hinkler

John Malam

Contents

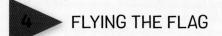

hinkler

Published by Hinkler Books Pty Ltd
45–55 Fairchild Street
Heatherton Victoria 3202 Australia
www.hinkler.com

© Hinkler Books Pty Ltd 2018

Author: John Malam
Packager: Tall Tree Ltd

ISBN: 978 1 4889 3637 1

Printed and bound in Malaysia

Welcome to the wonderful world of fascinating flags!

Full of symbolism and history, a flag represents the identity and spirit of a country. Every flag has its own exciting story to tell! The *Flags of the World Sticker Book* features loads of intriguing facts and oodles of information about the world we live in.

Explore these pages to discover answers to all sorts of interesting questions, such as:

▶ Which is the only flag that is not a square or rectangle?

▶ Which flag features an eagle holding a snake while perched on a cactus?

▶ Which country has a different flag depending on whether you are on land or at sea?

▶ What is the only two-sided flag in the world?

HOW TO USE THIS BOOK
In this book, the flags of the world are divided into nine regions.

Find the matching stickers for all the flags in the sticker pages and place them where marked on the nine maps found throughout the book.

Follow-on pages give extra facts and figures about a selection of countries in each region, and tell some of the fascinating stories behind their flags.

REGION PAGES

Maps illustrate each region of the world

FACT PAGES

Key information about specific countries

Find the matching flags in the sticker pages and stick them where marked

Where possible, official animals, trees, and sports have been listed for each country. If this hasn't been possible, unofficial or popular entries have been listed

Amazing flag facts and infographics

The name of each flag and when it was adopted

Flying the flag

Every country in the world has one thing in common: they all have their own national flag. The flag is a symbol of a country's identity, and something for people to take pride in. No two flags are exactly the same, and they can be recognized by their different colors and patterns.

PARTS OF A FLAG

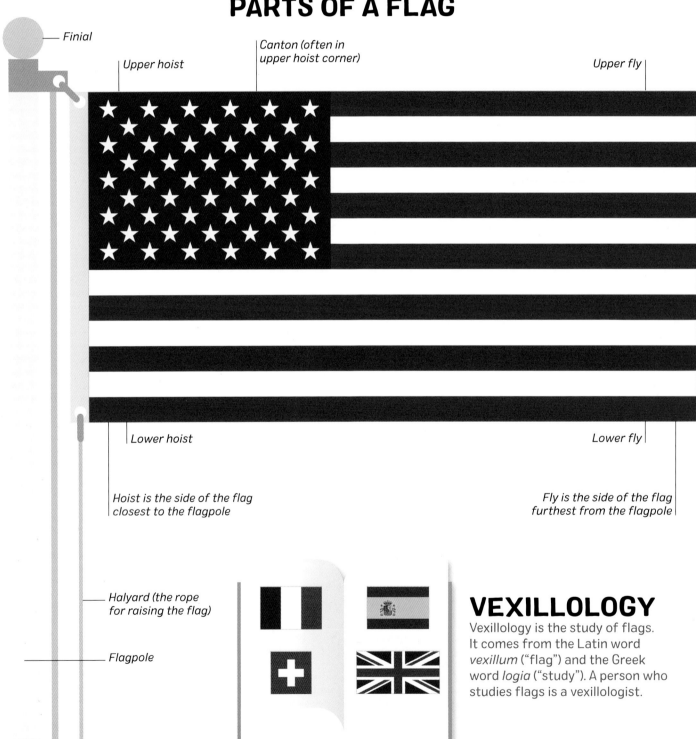

Finial

Upper hoist

Canton (often in upper hoist corner)

Upper fly

Lower hoist

Lower fly

Hoist is the side of the flag closest to the flagpole

Fly is the side of the flag furthest from the flagpole

Halyard (the rope for raising the flag)

Flagpole

VEXILLOLOGY

Vexillology is the study of flags. It comes from the Latin word *vexillum* ("flag") and the Greek word *logia* ("study"). A person who studies flags is a vexillologist.

RULES FOR FLYING A NATIONAL FLAG

It should be flown from sunrise to sunset.

It should be hoisted up quickly and lowered down slowly.

It should never touch the ground or water, or be used as a table cover.

When flown with flags from other countries, all the flagpoles should be the same height and the flags the same size.

When two flags are flown, the national flag should be on the left.

When three flags are flown, the national flag should be in the center.

A flag without a symmetrical design should be flown the right way up.

When a flag is flown as a sign of mourning, it should be flown at half mast.

A national flag must always be kept in good condition and replaced if it becomes damaged.

Countries of the world

All of the countries of the world have flags, but how many countries are there? It's a hard question to answer, as it all depends on what is meant by a "country." Let's look at some facts and figures.

7 CONTINENTS

44 countries in Europe

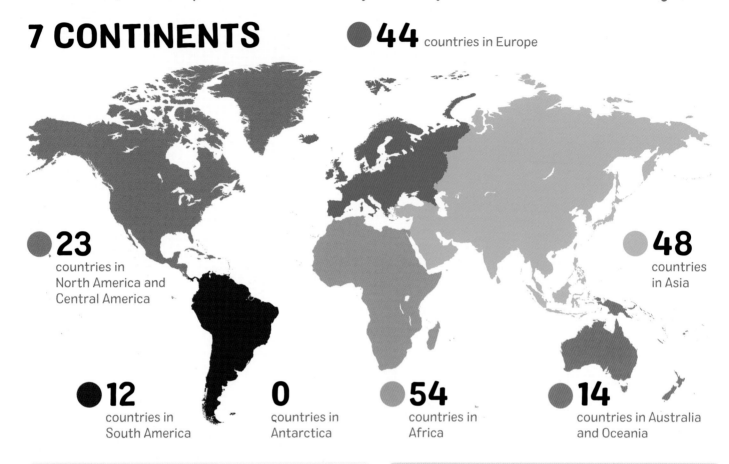

23
countries in North America and Central America

48
countries in Asia

12
countries in South America

0
countries in Antarctica

54
countries in Africa

14
countries in Australia and Oceania

FIVE OCEANS

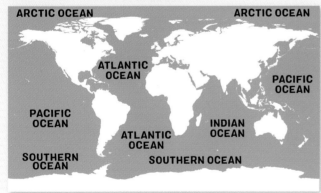

ARCTIC OCEAN   ARCTIC OCEAN
ATLANTIC OCEAN
PACIFIC OCEAN
PACIFIC OCEAN
INDIAN OCEAN
ATLANTIC OCEAN
SOUTHERN OCEAN   SOUTHERN OCEAN

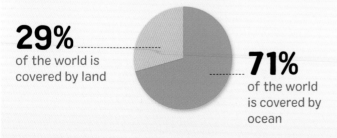

29%
of the world is covered by land

71%
of the world is covered by ocean

HOW MANY COUNTRIES ARE THERE?

Here are three ways to calculate the total number of countries in the world.

195

195 is the most widely accepted number, and is shown on the map above—it's the 193 United Nations members plus two observer states, Vatican City and the State of Palestine.

201

The 195, plus six countries that the UN partially recognizes (Taiwan, Western Sahara, Kosovo, South Ossetia, Abkhazia, and Northern Cyprus).

211

This is the number of countries who can compete in the soccer World Cup—England, Scotland, Wales, and Northern Ireland, for example, compete as separate teams, even though they're part of the United Kingdom.

TOP 5 BIGGEST COUNTRIES BY LAND

- **1** Russia
- **2** Canada
- **3** USA
- **4** China
- **5** Brazil

TOP 5 SMALLEST COUNTRIES BY LAND

1 Vatican City · 2 Monaco
3 Nauru · 4 Tuvalu · 5 San Marino

TOP 5 BIGGEST COUNTRIES BY POPULATION

- **1** China
- **2** India
- **3** USA
- **4** Indonesia
- **5** Brazil

TOP 5 SMALLEST COUNTRIES BY POPULATION

1 Vatican City · 2 Tuvalu
3 Nauru · 4 Palau · 5 San Marino

7

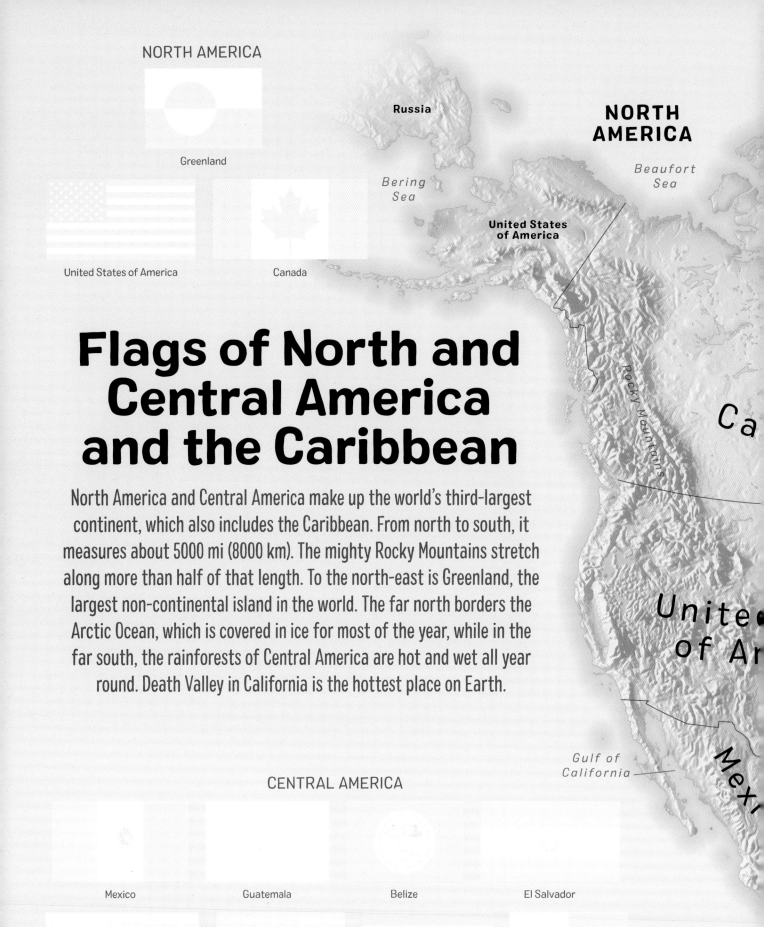

NORTH AMERICA

Greenland

United States of America

Canada

Flags of North and Central America and the Caribbean

North America and Central America make up the world's third-largest continent, which also includes the Caribbean. From north to south, it measures about 5000 mi (8000 km). The mighty Rocky Mountains stretch along more than half of that length. To the north-east is Greenland, the largest non-continental island in the world. The far north borders the Arctic Ocean, which is covered in ice for most of the year, while in the far south, the rainforests of Central America are hot and wet all year round. Death Valley in California is the hottest place on Earth.

CENTRAL AMERICA

Mexico

Guatemala

Belize

El Salvador

Honduras

Nicaragua

Costa Rica

Panama

Russia

Bering Sea

United States of America

NORTH AMERICA

Beaufort Sea

Rocky Mountains

Ca

Unite of Ar

Mexi

Gulf of California

PACIFIC OCEAN

ARCTIC OCEAN

Greenland

CARIBBEAN

Iceland

Baffin Bay

Antigua and Barbuda

Bahamas

Gulf of
St Lawrence

Saint Kitts and Nevis

Hudson
Bay

Cuba

da

Dominica

Dominican Republic

tates

Saint Lucia

rica

ATLANTIC
OCEAN

Haiti

Saint Vincent and the
Grenadines

Jamaica

CARIBBEAN

**Antigua and
Barbuda**

**Saint Kitts
and Nevis**

Bahamas

**Dominican
Republic**

Dominica

Barbados

Cuba

Haiti

**Saint Vincent
and the
Grenadines**

Saint Lucia

Gulf of Mexico

Jamaica

Barbados

Grenada

Belize

Caribbean Sea

**Trinidad and
Tobago**

Grenada

Honduras

Guatemala

Nicaragua

Costa Rica

El Salvador

**CENTRAL
AMERICA**

Panama

Trinidad and Tobago

9

Flags of North America and Central America

Canada

11-pointed maple leaf

Red for bravery, strength, and courage

FLAG PROFILE

Adopted: 1965

Called: *The Maple Leaf* or *l'Unifolié* (French for *"The One-leafed"*)

White for peace and honesty

POPULATION OVER 36.5 MILLION

CAPITAL OTTAWA

OFFICIAL LANGUAGES ENGLISH AND FRENCH

NATIONAL ANIMALS BEAVER AND CANADIAN HORSE

NATIONAL TREE MAPLE

NATIONAL SPORTS LACROSSE AND ICE HOCKEY

DID YOU KNOW?
Every weekday, a new flag is flown at the Peace Tower, at Parliament Hill, Ottawa. The old flag is given away to a Canadian resident. Thousands of Canadians have asked for a flag, and those at the bottom of the list will have to wait more than 70 years to get one!

FLAG PROFILE

Adopted: 1985

Called: *Erfalasorput* (Greenlandic for *"Our Flag"*)

Greenland

Red semi-circle for the sun

POPULATION OVER 58,000

CAPITAL NUUK

OFFICIAL LANGUAGES GREENLANDIC AND DANISH

NATIONAL ANIMAL POLAR BEAR

NATIONAL TREE GREYLEAF WILLOW

NATIONAL SPORT SOCCER

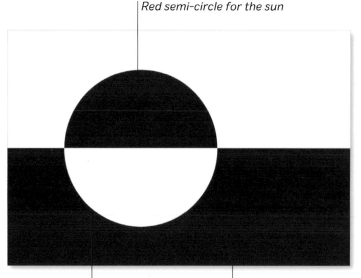

DID YOU KNOW?
Greenland is a territory of Denmark and has strong links with the Nordic countries of Denmark, Finland, Iceland, Norway, and Sweden. The flag is the only one in this group that does not have a Nordic cross on it.

White semi-circle for Greenland's ice

Red bar represents the ocean

United States of America

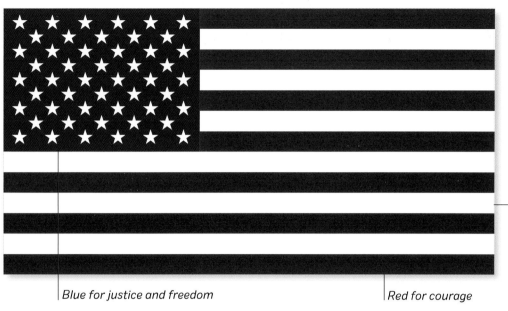

POPULATION OVER 323 MILLION
CAPITAL
WASHINGTON, D.C.
OFFICIAL LANGUAGE ENGLISH
NATIONAL ANIMALS BALD EAGLE AND AMERICAN BISON
NATIONAL TREE OAK
NATIONAL SPORT BASEBALL

White for purity

Blue for justice and freedom

Red for courage

FLAG PROFILE
Adopted: 1960
Called: *The Stars and Stripes* or *Old Glory*

DID YOU KNOW?
The 13 red and white stripes represent the 13 founding states of the United States of America. The 50 stars represent the present-day number of states. Star number 50 was added in 1960, after Hawaii joined the United States.

The tallest flagpole in the USA can be found at Sheboygan, Wisconsin. It is over 400 ft (120 m) tall—that's 98 ft (30 m) taller than the Statue of Liberty.

Mexico

POPULATION
OVER 124.5 MILLION
CAPITAL MEXICO CITY
OFFICIAL LANGUAGE SPANISH
NATIONAL ANIMALS GOLDEN EAGLE AND JAGUAR

NATIONAL TREE
MONTEZUMA CYPRESS
NATIONAL SPORT CHARRERÍA (SIMILAR TO RODEO)

Green for hope

White for purity

Red for courage

DID YOU KNOW?
Hundreds of years ago, the Aztecs, who were the original people of Mexico, were looking for a place to build their capital. Legend has it that Huitzilopochtli, god of the sun and war, told them to build it where they could see an eagle on top of a cactus, grasping a snake. The Aztec capital grew into Mexico City, and the eagle, snake, and cactus sit in the center of Mexico's flag.

FLAG PROFILE
Adopted: 1968
Called: *Bandera de México*
(Spanish for "Flag of Mexico")

Flags of the Caribbean

Barbados

POPULATION OVER 290,000
CAPITAL BRIDGETOWN
OFFICIAL LANGUAGE ENGLISH
NATIONAL ANIMAL DOLPHINFISH
NATIONAL TREE BEARDED FIG TREE
NATIONAL SPORT CRICKET

DID YOU KNOW?

In the center of the flag is the three-pronged trident of the mythical sea god Neptune. Its shaft is broken, to represent Barbados breaking away from Britain to become an independent country.

Gold for the sand of the island's beaches

Blue for the sea and sky of Barbados

FLAG PROFILE

Adopted: 1966
Called: *The Broken Trident*

Cuba

POPULATION OVER 11.2 MILLION
CAPITAL HAVANA
OFFICIAL LANGUAGE SPANISH
NATIONAL ANIMAL CUBAN TROGON (BIRD)
NATIONAL TREE ROYAL PALM
NATIONAL SPORT BASEBALL

Triangle for liberty, equality, and fraternity

White for purity

FLAG PROFILE

Adopted: 1902
Called: *La Estrella Solitaria* (Spanish for *"The Lone Star"*)

Three blue stripes for the three parts Cuba was once divided into

DID YOU KNOW?

At the time it became their national flag, many Cubans wanted Cuba to belong to the USA rather than Spain. For this reason, a white star was added to the flag to show that Cuba wanted to be a new state of the USA.

Puerto Rico

POPULATION OVER 3.3 MILLION
CAPITAL SAN JUAN
OFFICIAL LANGUAGES SPANISH AND ENGLISH
NATIONAL ANIMAL COQUÍ TREE FROG
NATIONAL TREE KAPOK
NATIONAL SPORT BASEBALL

DID YOU KNOW?
Puerto Rico, a territory of the USA, has flown its flag in space. NASA astronaut Joe Acaba took the flag on the space shuttle *Discovery* in 2009 and onto the International Space Station in 2017.

FLAG PROFILE

Adopted: 1952
Called: *Bandera de Puerto Rico* (Spanish for "Flag of Puerto Rico")

Star for the homeland of Puerto Rico

Red for courage

Triangle for the three branches of government

White for freedom

Jamaica

POPULATION OVER 2.8 MILLION
CAPITAL KINGSTON
OFFICIAL LANGUAGE ENGLISH
NATIONAL ANIMAL RED-BILLED STEAMERTAIL
NATIONAL TREE BLUE MAHOE
NATIONAL SPORT CRICKET

DID YOU KNOW?
The flag of Jamaica was designed by a Church of Scotland minister who worked in Jamaica. He based it on the flag of Scotland, replacing the blue and white of Scotland with the Jamaican colors of green, black, and gold.

Scotland

FLAG PROFILE

Adopted: 1962
Called: *The Cross*

Gold for natural resources and the beauty of sunlight

Black for hardship

Green for hope and agriculture

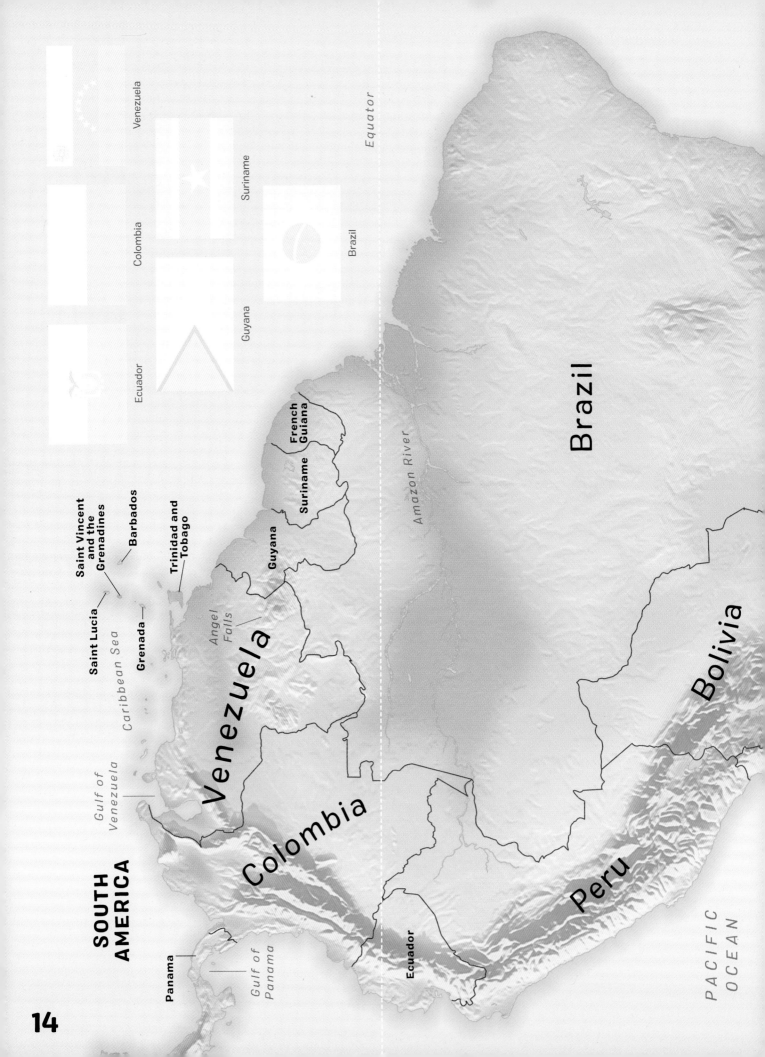

SOUTH AMERICA

Venezuela

Colombia

Ecuador

Suriname

Brazil

Guyana

Panama

Saint Vincent and the Grenadines

Barbados

Saint Lucia

Grenada

Trinidad and Tobago

Caribbean Sea

Gulf of Venezuela

Gulf of Panama

Colombia

Venezuela

Angel Falls

Guyana

Suriname

French Guiana

Equator

Amazon River

Brazil

Ecuador

Peru

Bolivia

PACIFIC OCEAN

Flags of South America

South America is the world's fourth-largest continent. From north to south it measures about 4700 mi (7500 km), and at its widest point, through Peru and Brazil, it is about 3300 mi (5300 km). The continent has the driest place on Earth (Atacama Desert, Chile), the highest waterfall (Angel Falls, Venezuela), and the world's longest mountain range (the Andes). The mighty Amazon River flows for 3950 mi (6400 km) through Peru, Colombia, and Brazil. Puerto Williams in Chile is the world's most southerly town, and is the place from which scientists travel to Antarctica.

SOUTH
ATLANTIC
OCEAN

Paraguay

Uruguay

Argentina

Chile

Andes Mountains

Atacama Desert

Strait of Magellan

Cape Horn

Puerto Williams

Peru

Bolivia

Chile

Paraguay

Uruguay

Argentina

Flags of South America

Argentina

POPULATION OVER 44.2 MILLION
CAPITAL BUENOS AIRES
OFFICIAL LANGUAGE SPANISH
NATIONAL ANIMAL RED OVENBIRD
NATIONAL TREES COCKSPUR CORAL TREE AND RED QUEBRACHO
NATIONAL SPORT PATO (SIMILAR TO POLO)

FLAG PROFILE

Adopted: 1818

Called: *La Albiceleste* **(Spanish for "White and Sky Blue One")**

DID YOU KNOW?

In the center of the flag is the *Sol de Mayo* (Spanish for "May Sun"), the national emblem of Argentina. It represents the sun that shone through cloudy skies in May 1810, during the first big demonstration in favor of independence from Spain.

Blue for the clear sky

May Sun emblem

White for the snow of the Andes Mountains

Brazil

POPULATION OVER 207.3 MILLION
CAPITAL BRASÍLIA
OFFICIAL LANGUAGE PORTUGUESE
NATIONAL ANIMALS JAGUAR AND RED-BELLIED THRUSH
NATIONAL TREE BRAZILWOOD
NATIONAL SPORT CAPOEIRA (MARTIAL ART)

DID YOU KNOW?

The stars are for the 26 Brazilian states and the Federal District. They are from constellations in the Southern Hemisphere, and show them as they appeared above Rio de Janeiro at 8:30am on November 15, 1889—the day Brazil became a republic.

Green for agriculture

Yellow for gold for the wealth of Brazil

ORDEM E PROGRESSO

FLAG PROFILE

Adopted: 1992

Called: *A Auriverde* **(Portuguese for "Yellow and Green One")**

Dark blue for the night sky, with 27 stars

Motto along equator: Ordem e Progresso (Portuguese for "Order and Progress")

15
November
1889

Paraguay

POPULATION OVER 6.9 MILLION

CAPITAL ASUNCIÓN

OFFICIAL LANGUAGES
SPANISH AND GUARANÍ

NATIONAL ANIMAL
PAMPAS FOX

NATIONAL TREE
PINK TRUMPET TREE

NATIONAL SPORT
SOCCER

Red for patriotism and bravery

Star of May, an emblem of independence

Blue for freedom

DID YOU KNOW?
The flag of Paraguay is the world's only two-sided flag. The colors are the same on both sides, but the emblems in the middle of the flag are different. On the front is the coat of arms of Paraguay, and on the back is the seal of the government treasury department.

Reverse of flag

Guyana

POPULATION OVER 737,000

CAPITAL GEORGETOWN

OFFICIAL LANGUAGE ENGLISH

NATIONAL ANIMAL JAGUAR

NATIONAL FLOWER VICTORIA AMAZONICA (WORLD'S LARGEST WATERLILY)

NATIONAL SPORTS CRICKET AND WATER POLO

DID YOU KNOW?
A flag is a symbol of independence. At midnight on May 25, 1966, the British Union Jack, which had flown over Guyana for 163 years, was lowered for the last time and the new flag of Guyana, the Golden Arrowhead, was raised.

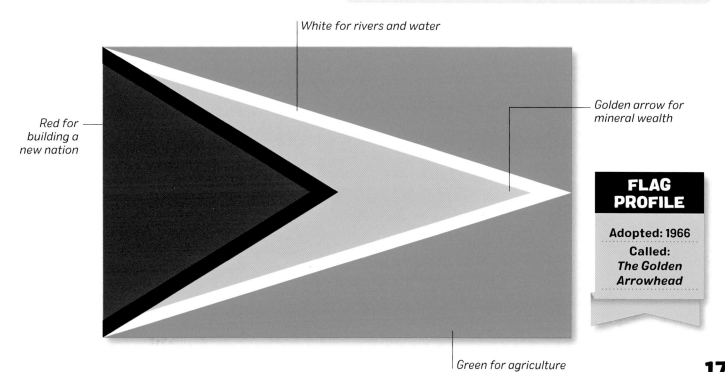

White for rivers and water

Golden arrow for mineral wealth

Red for building a new nation

Green for agriculture

Flags of Western Europe and Scandinavia

Europe is the second-smallest continent, after Australia, though some geographers classify Europe and Asia as the same continent, called Eurasia. Some of the world's smallest countries are found in Western Europe, including the tiny nation of Monaco. With more than 60,000 people per square mile, Monaco is the world's most densely populated country. Sitting just south of the Arctic Circle, Iceland is the most sparsely populated country in Europe, with a cold climate and many active volcanoes. On the island of Sicily in Italy, Mount Etna is one of the most active volcanoes in the world. It continuously spews lava from its summit, and larger eruptions take place every few years.

Finland

Sweden

Iceland

SCANDINAVIA

Norway

Denmark

United Kingdom

Finland

Gulf of Finland

Baltic Sea

Gulf of Bothnia

Sweden

Norway

Norwegian Sea

North Sea

Iceland

ARCTIC OCEAN

ATLANTIC OCEAN

WESTERN EUROPE

Belgium

Switzerland

Netherlands

Germany

Luxembourg

Austria

Germany

San Marino

Liechtenstein

Italy

United Kingdom

Germany

Netherlands

Belgium

Luxembourg

Austria

Liechtenstein

Switzerland

San Marino

Italy

Malta

Vatican City

Tyrrhenian Sea

Monaco

English Channel

France

Mediterranean Sea

Monaco

Andorra

Malta

Ireland

France

Andorra

Spain

Spain

Portugal

Portugal

Flags of Western Europe

France

POPULATION OVER 67.1 MILLION
CAPITAL PARIS
OFFICIAL LANGUAGE FRENCH
NATIONAL ANIMAL GALLIC ROOSTER
NATIONAL FLOWER IRIS
NATIONAL SPORT SOCCER

DID YOU KNOW?

France has different flags for land and sea. The land flag has three stripes of equal width. The sea flag has a narrower blue and a wider red stripe. This is to give a good visual effect when flying, making the stripes appear the same width (this is known as "optical proportions").

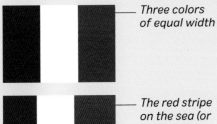

Three colors of equal width

The red stripe on the sea (or ensign) flag is slightly wider

Blue and red for the colors of the city of Paris

White for the old monarchy of the Royal House of Bourbon

FLAG PROFILE

Adopted: 1794
Called: *Le Tricolore* (French for "*The Three Colors*")

The same three colors were seen on cockades (also known as rosettes) worn on hats during the French Revolution in 1789.

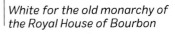

Switzerland

POPULATION OVER 8.2 MILLION
CAPITAL BERN
OFFICIAL LANGUAGES GERMAN, FRENCH, ITALIAN, AND ROMANSH
NATIONAL ANIMAL CHAMOIS (A GOAT-ANTELOPE)
NATIONAL TREE LIME
NATIONAL SPORT SCHWINGEN (WRESTLING)

FLAG PROFILE

Adopted: 1889
Called: *The Swiss Cross*

Rectangular version

DID YOU KNOW?

The flag of Switzerland is square—most of the time. When the flag is flown on boats and ships, at sea, and on the country's lakes, a rectangular version is used. The other place to see a rectangular Swiss flag is at the Olympic Games, where country flags are the same size to show that everyone is equal.

Holy Cross, used on Swiss flags since the 1300s

Spain

POPULATION OVER 48.9 MILLION
CAPITAL MADRID
OFFICIAL LANGUAGE SPANISH
NATIONAL ANIMAL BULL
NATIONAL TREE EVERGREEN OAK
NATIONAL SPORT SOCCER

DID YOU KNOW?

The largest Spanish flag in the world measures 46 ft x 69 ft (14 m x 21 m). It flies from a flagpole which is 164 ft (50 m) high, in the Plaza de Colón, Madrid. It gets blown about so much by the wind, it soon becomes tatty and has to be replaced three times every year.

Coat of arms of Spain

Red and yellow symbolize the ancient kingdoms of Spain

Spain's largest flag is around 500 times the size of a person.

FLAG PROFILE

Adopted: 1981
Called: *La Rojigualda* (Spanish for "Red-weld;" weld is a plant with yellow flowers)

United Kingdom

The UK flag combines the crosses of the flags of nations that are officially part of the United Kingdom.

Cross of St George (patron saint of England)

Cross of St Patrick (patron saint of Ireland)

Cross of St Andrew (patron saint of Scotland)

POPULATION OVER 65.5 MILLION
CAPITAL LONDON
OFFICIAL LANGUAGE ENGLISH
NATIONAL ANIMALS LION AND BULLDOG
NATIONAL TREE OAK
NATIONAL SPORTS SOCCER, CRICKET, RUGBY, AND GOLF

DID YOU KNOW?

The UK flag is not symmetrical. Look closely and you'll see it has a top and bottom. The correct way to fly it is with the wide white diagonal stripe at the top left of the flag. If it's flown with the narrow white diagonal stripe at the top left, then the flag is upside-down. An upside-down flag is only meant to be used as a distress signal.

FLAG PROFILE

Adopted: 1801
Called: The Union Flag or The Union Jack

Flags of Scandinavia

Denmark

Red for courage

DID YOU KNOW?

The flag of Denmark is the oldest national flag in the world that is still in use today. According to legend, a red flag with a white cross fell from heaven in 1219, during a battle in Estonia. The flag gave the Danes hope, and they won the battle.

POPULATION OVER 5.6 MILLION
CAPITAL COPENHAGEN
OFFICIAL LANGUAGE DANISH
NATIONAL ANIMAL MUTE SWAN
NATIONAL TREE BEECH
NATIONAL SPORT SOCCER

FLAG PROFILE
Adopted: 1625
Called: *Dannebrog* (Danish for "*The flag of the Danes*" or "*The Red Flag*")

Sweden

POPULATION OVER 9.9 MILLION
CAPITAL STOCKHOLM
OFFICIAL LANGUAGE SWEDISH
NATIONAL ANIMAL ELK
NATIONAL TREE ORNÄS BIRCH
NATIONAL SPORT SOCCER

DID YOU KNOW?

The flag was adopted in 1906, but similar flags had been around for hundreds of years. The current flag was adopted when Sweden and Norway separated into two countries.

FLAG PROFILE

Adopted: 1906
Called: *Svenska flaggan* (Swedish for "*Swedish Flag*")

Blue and gold, from the colors of Sweden's coat of arms

Norway

POPULATION OVER 5.3 MILLION
CAPITAL OSLO
OFFICIAL LANGUAGE NORWEGIAN
NATIONAL ANIMAL ELK
NATIONAL FLOWER PURPLE HEATHER
NATIONAL SPORT CROSS-COUNTRY SKIING

FLAG PROFILE

Adopted: 1821
Called:
Dannebrogelva
(Danish–Norwegian for *"Danish Flag and River"*)

Blue for links with Sweden

Red and white for links with Denmark

DID YOU KNOW?
The flag of Norway was the first flag to fly at the South Pole. It was raised there on December 14, 1911, when Norwegian explorer Roald Amundsen became the first person to reach the southernmost point on Earth.

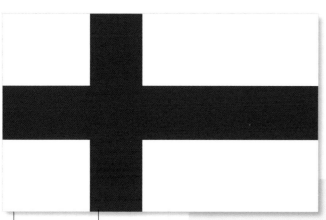

White for the winter snow

Blue for Finland's lakes and clear sky

Finland

POPULATION OVER 5.5 MILLION
CAPITAL HELSINKI
OFFICIAL LANGUAGE FINNISH
NATIONAL ANIMAL BROWN BEAR
NATIONAL TREE SILVER BIRCH
NATIONAL SPORT PESÄPALLO (SIMILAR TO BASEBALL)

DID YOU KNOW?
Finland was 100 years old in 2017. To mark this, the government made Finnish Nature Day (the last Saturday in August) an official flag day. Finland was the first country in the world to fly its national flag for nature.

FLAG PROFILE

Adopted: 1918
Called:
Siniristilippu
(Finnish for *"Blue Cross Flag"*)

Iceland

POPULATION OVER 339,000
CAPITAL REYKJAVIK
OFFICIAL LANGUAGE ICELANDIC
NATIONAL ANIMAL GYRFALCON
NATIONAL FLOWER MOUNTAIN AVENS
NATIONAL SPORT HANDBALL

Red for links with Norway, and for Iceland's volcanoes

FLAG PROFILE

Adopted: 1944
Called:
íslenski fáninn
(Icelandic for *"Flag of Iceland"*)

DID YOU KNOW?
In Iceland, the national flag cannot be flown before seven o'clock in the morning, and it should be taken down at sunset—that's the law!

Flags of Southern and Eastern Europe

Eastern Europe is dominated by a single massive country—Russia. It is so vast that it stretches across two continents—Europe to the west, and Asia to the east. Many regard the Ural Mountains, which run north to south through western Russia, as the boundary between Europe and Asia. Another European link with Asia is Turkey, where a small part lies on mainland Europe, but the bulk of the country is in Asia. The boundary between the two is the Bosphorus, a narrow strait of sea.

Russia

Belarus

Poland

White Sea

Gulf of Finland

Estonia

Latvia

Lithuania

Russia

EASTERN EUROPE

Baltic Sea

Estonia

Belarus

Lithuania

Russia

Latvia

Poland

Sea of
Azov

Ukraine

Moldova

Romania

Black
Sea

Bosphorus

Bulgaria

Turkey

ASIA

Hungary

Slovakia

Czech Republic

Serbia

TFYR
Macedonia

Albania

Aegean
Sea

Greece

Montenegro

Bosnia and
Herzegovina

Croatia

Slovenia

Ionian Sea

SOUTHERN
EUROPE

Adriatic Sea

Italy

Ukraine

Moldova

Romania

Bulgaria

The Former Yugoslav
Republic of Macedonia

Greece

Montenegro

Albania

Czech Republic

Slovakia

Hungary

Slovenia

Croatia

Serbia

Bosnia and Herzegovina

Flags of Southern and Eastern Europe

Czech Republic

POPULATION OVER 10.6 MILLION

CAPITAL PRAGUE

OFFICIAL LANGUAGE CZECH

NATIONAL ANIMAL
DOUBLE-TAILED LION
(AN ANCIENT SYMBOL)

NATIONAL TREE LIME

NATIONAL SPORTS
ICE HOCKEY AND SOCCER

Red and white for the region of Bohemia

Blue for the region of Moravia

FLAG PROFILE

Adopted: 1993

Called: *Státni vlajka České republiky (Czech for "The National Flag of the Czech Republic")*

DID YOU KNOW?
The flag of the Czech Republic is the same as the flag of the former Czechoslovakia. In 1993, Czechoslovakia split up to form the Czech Republic and Slovakia. While Slovakia brought in a new flag, the Czech Republic kept the old one.

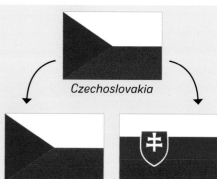

Czechoslovakia

Czech Republic

Slovakia

Greece

POPULATION OVER 10.7 MILLION

CAPITAL ATHENS

OFFICIAL LANGUAGE GREEK

NATIONAL ANIMAL DOLPHIN

NATIONAL TREE
OLIVE

NATIONAL SPORT
SOCCER

Cross for the Greek Orthodox church

White for the waves on the sea

Blue for the sea and sky

FLAG PROFILE

Adopted: 1822

Called:
Galanolefci (Greek for the "Blue and White")

DID YOU KNOW?
There is no official color for the exact shade of blue used for the Greek flag. For this reason, flags range from light blue to dark blue—and they are all considered correct.

Albania

Double-headed eagle

Red for bravery and courage

POPULATION OVER 3 MILLION
CAPITAL TIRANA
OFFICIAL LANGUAGE ALBANIAN
NATIONAL ANIMAL GOLDEN EAGLE
NATIONAL TREE OLIVE
NATIONAL SPORT SOCCER

DID YOU KNOW?
According to a myth, the Albanian people are descended from an eagle. They call themselves the "Sons of the Eagle". This is why the flag of Albania has an eagle on it.

Over the years, different rulers of Albania have changed the look of their flag. For example, in 1946, the communist government added a yellow star above the eagle.

FLAG PROFILE
Adopted: 1912
Called: *Flamuri Kombëtar* (Albanian for "National Flag")

Russia

POPULATION OVER 142 MILLION
CAPITAL MOSCOW
OFFICIAL LANGUAGE RUSSIAN
NATIONAL ANIMAL BROWN BEAR
NATIONAL TREE SIBERIAN FIR
NATIONAL SPORTS SOCCER AND ICE HOCKEY

DID YOU KNOW?
The flag of Russia is based on the flag of the Netherlands (Holland). In 1697, Peter the Great, the ruler of Russia, saw the Dutch flag. He liked the simple design of red–white–blue bands, and changed their order to white–blue–red to create the Russian flag.

Blue for honesty

White for generosity

Red for courage

Netherlands

Up until 1991, the flag under the Soviet Union was red with a gold hammer, sickle, and star on top.

FLAG PROFILE
Adopted: 1993
Called: *Trikolor* ("*Tricolor*") for its three bands of colors

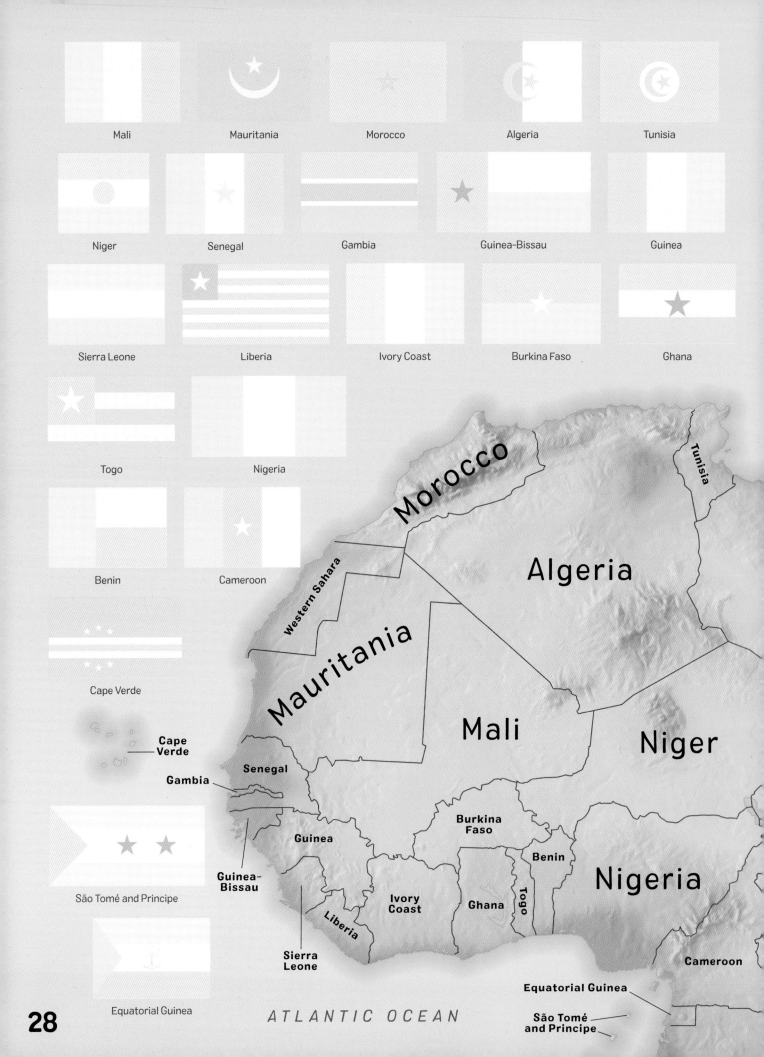

Mali

Mauritania

Morocco

Algeria

Tunisia

Niger

Senegal

Gambia

Guinea-Bissau

Guinea

Sierra Leone

Liberia

Ivory Coast

Burkina Faso

Ghana

Togo

Nigeria

Benin

Cameroon

Cape Verde

São Tomé and Principe

Equatorial Guinea

Morocco

Tunisia

Algeria

Western Sahara

Mauritania

Mali

Niger

Cape Verde

Senegal

Gambia

Guinea

Guinea-Bissau

Burkina Faso

Benin

Ivory Coast

Ghana

Togo

Nigeria

Liberia

Sierra Leone

Cameroon

Equatorial Guinea

São Tomé and Principe

ATLANTIC OCEAN

Flags of Northern Africa

Africa is the second-largest continent, with about 20% of all land on Earth. To the north, Africa borders the Mediterranean Sea. Much of northern Africa, from Mauritania in the west to Egypt in the east, is covered by the sandy Sahara Desert, the world's largest hot desert. In the north-east flows the River Nile, the world's longest river at 4258 mi (6853 km) long. South Sudan is one of the world's newest countries, having been created in 2011.

Libya

Chad

Central African Republic

Egypt

Eritrea

Sudan

Djibouti

South Sudan

Ethiopia

Somalia

Gulf of Sirte

Mediterranean Sea

Libya

Egypt

Red Sea

Chad

Sudan

Eritrea

Djibouti

Gulf of Aden

Central African Republic

South Sudan

Ethiopia

Somalia

INDIAN OCEAN

Flags of Northern Africa

Algeria

Green, to represent Islam

White for peace

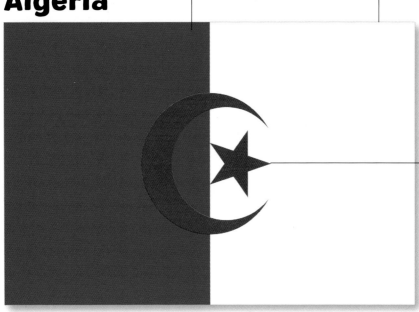

POPULATION OVER 40. 9 MILLION
CAPITAL ALGIERS
OFFICIAL LANGUAGE ARABIC
NATIONAL ANIMAL FENNEC FOX
NATIONAL FLOWER IRIS
NATIONAL SPORT SOCCER

Star and crescent, symbols of Islam

Algeria has strict laws forbidding people from insulting the flag. Anyone disrespecting the flag can be sent to prison.

DID YOU KNOW?
Algeria, like some other Muslim countries, uses a crescent moon symbol on its flag. However, Algeria's crescent is more circular than most. Algerians believe that the long, curved points on the crescent are a symbol of good luck for the nation.

FLAG PROFILE

Adopted: 1962
Called: *Flag of the Democratic and Popular Republic of Algeria*

FLAG PROFILE

Adopted: 1984

Inscription: *Jumhuriyat Misr al-Arabiya* (Arab Republic of Egypt)

Egypt

POPULATION OVER 97 MILLION
CAPITAL CAIRO
OFFICIAL LANGUAGE ARABIC
NATIONAL ANIMAL STEPPE EAGLE
NATIONAL FLOWER LOTUS OR WATERLILY
NATIONAL SPORT SOCCER

Red for when Egypt was ruled by a king

White for the 1952 revolution that overthrew the king

DID YOU KNOW?
There are strict rules about flying the national flag in Egypt. For example, all government buildings must fly the flag every Friday, and at other times if the government says so.

Black for Egypt's modern government

Eagle of Saladin for Arab unity

Blue square for Africa

Liberia

POPULATION OVER 4.6 MILLION

CAPITAL MONROVIA

OFFICIAL LANGUAGE ENGLISH

NATIONAL ANIMAL LION

NATIONAL FLOWER
PEPPER FLOWER

NATIONAL SPORT SOCCER

FLAG PROFILE
Adopted: 1847
Called: The *Lone Star*

Star for freedom granted to ex-slaves

11 stripes for the 11 men who signed the Liberian Declaration of Independence

DID YOU KNOW?
The flag of Liberia is based on the Stars and Stripes of the USA. This is because Liberia began as a home for freed American slaves (Liberia is from the Latin word *liber*, meaning "free").

United States of America

Ethiopia

POPULATION OVER 105.3 MILLION

CAPITAL ADDIS ABABA

OFFICIAL LANGUAGES
AMHARIC AND OTHERS

NATIONAL ANIMAL LION

NATIONAL FLOWER CALLA LILY

NATIONAL SPORTS
ATHLETICS AND SOCCER

FLAG PROFILE
Adopted: 1996
Called: *Flag of Ethiopia*

Green for the fertility of the land

Red for courage and sacrifice

Five-pointed star for the equality of Ethiopian peoples

Gold for freedom and peace

DID YOU KNOW?
Ethiopia is the oldest independent country in Africa. As other countries in Africa gained their independence, they used the same colors on their flags, in admiration of Ethiopia. They are known as the Pan-African colors (meaning "all African").

Up until 1974, the flag of Ethiopia featured the Lion of Judah.

Gabon

Congo

Democratic Republic of the Congo

Angola

Flags of Central and Southern Africa

In contrast to the drier north, central Africa is known for its tropical rainforests. The forests begin on the western coast at Gabon and continue down through Congo to the Democratic Republic of the Congo. The Namib Desert runs further south along the west coast, stretching from Angola to South Africa. Africa's highest mountain, Mount Kilimanjaro (19,341 ft/5895 m), is found in Tanzania, while the continent's largest lake, Lake Victoria, straddles the borders of Uganda, Kenya, and Tanzania.

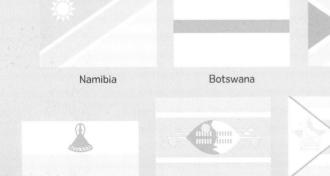

Namibia

Botswana

South Africa

Lesotho

Swaziland

Zimbabwe

Gabon

Congo

Equator

Democratic Republic of the Congo

Angola

Namibia

Botswana

South Africa

ATLANTIC OCEAN

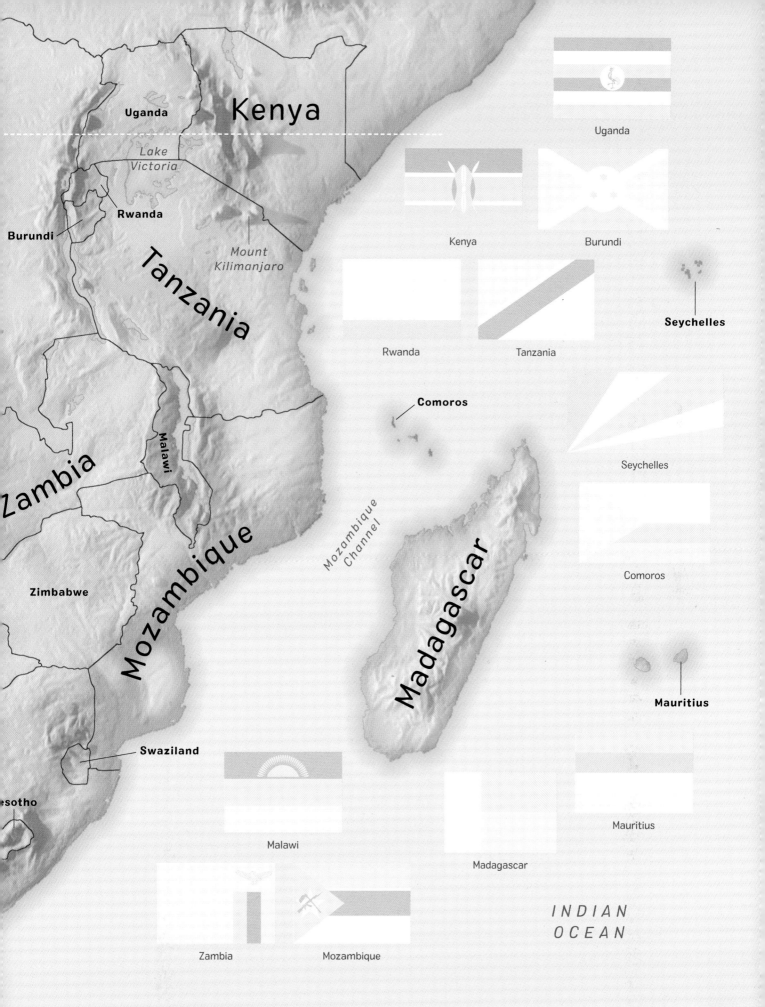

Uganda

Kenya

Burundi

Seychelles

Rwanda

Tanzania

Seychelles

Comoros

Mauritius

Malawi

Mauritius

Madagascar

Zambia

Mozambique

INDIAN
OCEAN

Uganda

Kenya

Lake
Victoria

Rwanda

Burundi

Tanzania

Mount
Kilimanjaro

Malawi

Zambia

Mozambique

Zimbabwe

Comoros

Madagascar

Swaziland

Lesotho

33

Flags of Central and Southern Africa

Botswana

POPULATION OVER 2.2 MILLION
CAPITAL GABORONE
OFFICIAL LANGUAGE ENGLISH
NATIONAL ANIMAL ZEBRA
NATIONAL TREE MARULA
NATIONAL SPORT SOCCER

Blue for rain

FLAG PROFILE

Adopted: 1966

Called: The *National Flag of Botswana*

Black and white for the stripes of the national animal, the zebra. The stripes also represent people of different racial backgrounds working together in harmony.

DID YOU KNOW?
The flag of Botswana does not use red, green, and gold—the colors of many African flags. Instead, blue was chosen as the main color because of the country's motto—"Let there be rain." Botswana is a dry country, and rain is a precious resource.

Kenya

POPULATION OVER 47. 6 MILLION
CAPITAL NAIROBI
OFFICIAL LANGUAGES ENGLISH AND SWAHILI
NATIONAL ANIMAL LION
NATIONAL TREE ACACIA
NATIONAL SPORT SOCCER

FLAG PROFILE

Adopted: 1963

Called: *Flag of Kenya* or in Swahili *"Bendera"*

Red for sacrifice in the fight for independence

Black for the Kenyan people

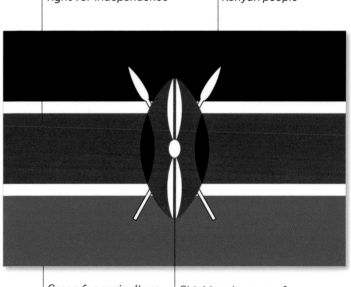

DID YOU KNOW?
The Maasai people live in the south of Kenya. A traditional Maasai warrior's shield and two spears appear on the flag of Kenya, to show that Kenyan people will defend their country.

Green for agriculture

Shield and spears of Maasai people

Democratic Republic of the Congo

Star for bright future

Yellow for wealth

Red for sacrifice

Sky blue for peace and hope

POPULATION OVER 83.3 MILLION
CAPITAL KINSHASA
OFFICIAL LANGUAGE FRENCH
NATIONAL ANIMAL OKAPI (RELATED TO THE GIRAFFE)
NATIONAL FLOWER FLAME LILY
NATIONAL SPORT SOCCER

FLAG PROFILE

Adopted: 2006

Called: The *Flag of the Democratic Republic of the Congo*

DID YOU KNOW?
The Democratic Republic of the Congo came into existence in 1997. Since then, the country has had three different flags. The latest flag is similar to one last used in the 1960s, but it had a dark blue background.

South Africa

POPULATION OVER 56.5 MILLION
CAPITALS
PRETORIA, BLOEMFONTEIN, AND CAPE TOWN
OFFICIAL LANGUAGES
AFRIKAANS, ENGLISH, AND OTHERS
NATIONAL ANIMAL SPRINGBOK (A TYPE OF ANTELOPE)
NATIONAL TREE REAL YELLOWWOOD
NATIONAL SPORTS SOCCER, RUGBY, AND CRICKET

DID YOU KNOW?
The design of the flag is based around a "V" shape that transforms into a "Y" shape going across the flag horizontally. It represents the different communities of South Africa coming together as one united people. The flag's colors are drawn from the flags of the ANC and the old South African Republic.

ANC

South African Republic

Yellow, black, and green are the colors of the African National Congress (ANC), an organization that seeks to end racism and injustice

Red, white, and blue are old colors of South Africa

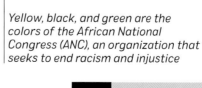

FLAG PROFILE

Adopted: 1994

Called: The *Rainbow Flag* (unofficially)

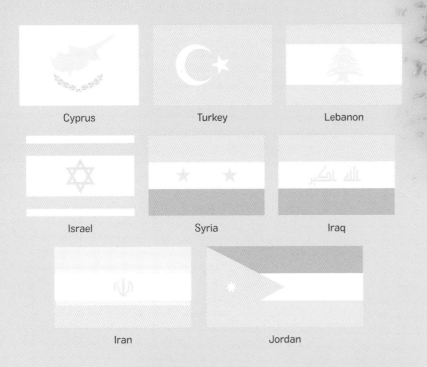

Cyprus

Turkey

Lebanon

Israel

Syria

Iraq

Iran

Jordan

Mediterranean Sea

Cyprus

Lebanon

State of Palestine

Dead Sea

Israel

Jordan

Red Sea

Flags of the Middle East

The Middle East is a region of western Asia, centered on the Arabian Peninsula. It is an area of deserts, grasslands, mountains, and marshes. The fertile land around the rivers Tigris and Euphrates in Iraq, known as Mesopotamia, was the location of some of the world's first great civilizations. On the borders of Jordan, Israel, and Palestine is a giant lake known as the Dead Sea (about 42 mi/67 km long). A saltwater lake about nine times saltier than the ocean, the Dead Sea is the lowest point on Earth at around 1378 ft (420 m) below sea level.

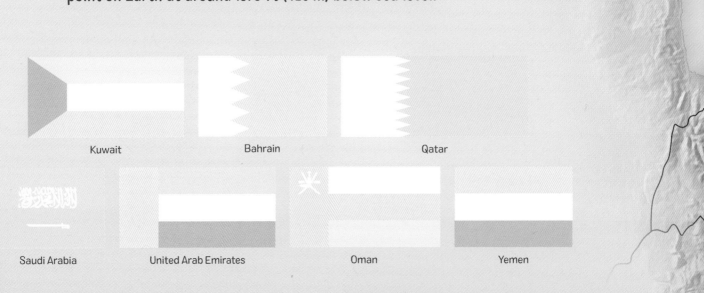

Kuwait

Bahrain

Qatar

Saudi Arabia

United Arab Emirates

Oman

Yemen

yria

Iraq

Iran

Caspian
Sea

Kuwait

Persian Gulf

Bahrain

Qatar

Strait of
Hormuz

Gulf of
Oman

Saudi
Arabia

United Arab
Emirates

Oman

Yemen

Arabian
Sea

Gulf of Aden

37

Flags of the Middle East

United Arab Emirates

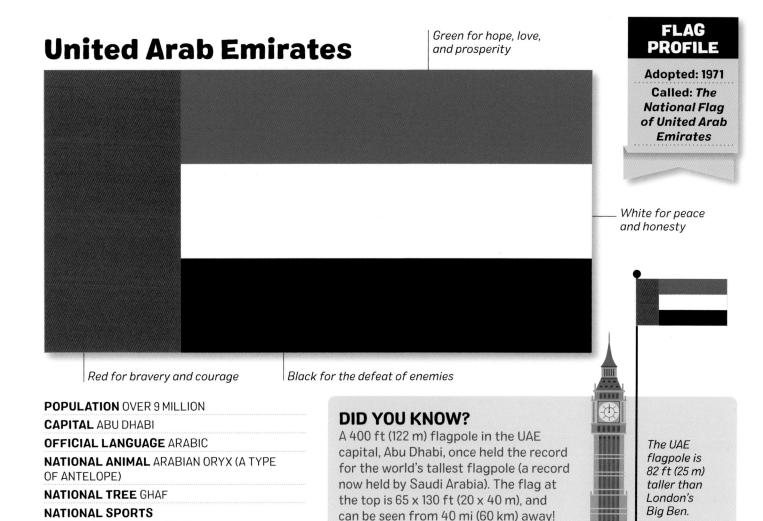

Green for hope, love, and prosperity

White for peace and honesty

Red for bravery and courage

Black for the defeat of enemies

FLAG PROFILE

Adopted: 1971

Called: *The National Flag of United Arab Emirates*

POPULATION OVER 9 MILLION

CAPITAL ABU DHABI

OFFICIAL LANGUAGE ARABIC

NATIONAL ANIMAL ARABIAN ORYX (A TYPE OF ANTELOPE)

NATIONAL TREE GHAF

NATIONAL SPORTS SOCCER AND CAMEL RACING

DID YOU KNOW?
A 400 ft (122 m) flagpole in the UAE capital, Abu Dhabi, once held the record for the world's tallest flagpole (a record now held by Saudi Arabia). The flag at the top is 65 x 130 ft (20 x 40 m), and can be seen from 40 mi (60 km) away!

The UAE flagpole is 82 ft (25 m) taller than London's Big Ben.

FLAG PROFILE

Adopted: 1943

Called: *The National Flag of Lebanon*

Lebanon

POPULATION OVER 6 MILLION

CAPITAL BEIRUT

OFFICIAL LANGUAGE ARABIC

NATIONAL ANIMAL STRIPED HYENA

NATIONAL TREE LEBANON CEDAR

NATIONAL SPORT SOCCER

Cedar tree, a symbol of holiness and peace

DID YOU KNOW?
The cedar tree on the flag of Lebanon is all green, even the trunk and branches. Lebanese flags have been made with the trunk and branches colored brown, just as they are in real life, but this is a mistake. The law says the tree must be green.

White for mountain snow, purity, and peace

Red for sacrifice in the struggle for independence

Qatar

POPULATION OVER 2 MILLION

CAPITAL DOHA

OFFICIAL LANGUAGE ARABIC

NATIONAL ANIMAL ARABIAN ORYX (A TYPE OF ANTELOPE)

NATIONAL TREE SIDRA / CHRIST'S THORN JUJUBE

NATIONAL SPORT SOCCER

White for peace

Nine white points for the nine Arab states (including Qatar) that signed the Qatari-British treaty in 1916

DID YOU KNOW?

The flag of Qatar was originally bright red, and was almost identical to the flag of neighboring Bahrain. To avoid confusion, the color was changed to maroon (dark purple), and the flag's shape became long and thin.

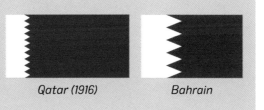

Qatar (1916)

Bahrain

Turkey

POPULATION OVER 80. 8 MILLION

CAPITAL ANKARA

OFFICIAL LANGUAGE TURKISH

NATIONAL ANIMAL GREY WOLF

NATIONAL FLOWER TULIP

NATIONAL SPORT OIL WRESTLING

Star and crescent, symbols of Islam

DID YOU KNOW?

If a straight line was drawn between the two points of the crescent moon, the left-hand point of the star would just touch it. The star originally had eight points, until it was changed to five in about 1844.

The star and crescent symbols were also used by the mighty Ottoman rulers in Turkey from 1453 to 1923.

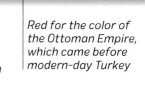

Red for the color of the Ottoman Empire, which came before modern-day Turkey

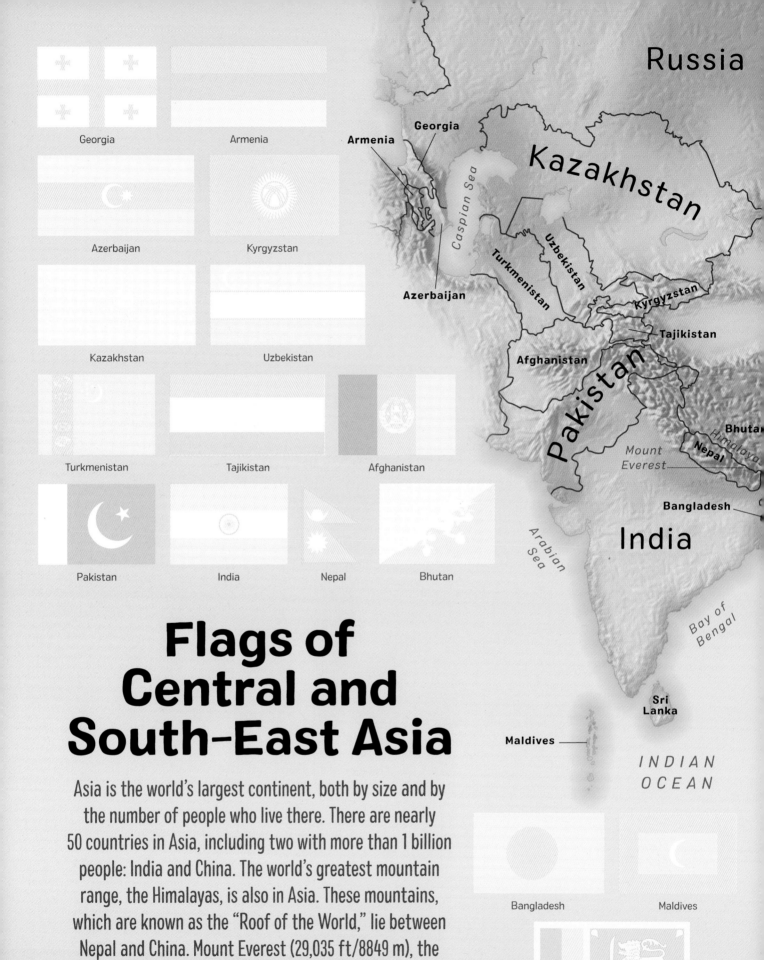

Georgia

Armenia

Azerbaijan

Kyrgyzstan

Kazakhstan

Uzbekistan

Turkmenistan

Tajikistan

Afghanistan

Pakistan

India

Nepal

Bhutan

Russia

Kazakhstan

Georgia

Armenia

Azerbaijan

Caspian Sea

Turkmenistan

Uzbekistan

Kyrgyzstan

Tajikistan

Afghanistan

Pakistan

Himalayas

Bhutan

Nepal

Mount Everest

Bangladesh

India

Arabian Sea

Bay of Bengal

Sri Lanka

Maldives

INDIAN OCEAN

Bangladesh

Maldives

Sri Lanka

Flags of Central and South-East Asia

Asia is the world's largest continent, both by size and by the number of people who live there. There are nearly 50 countries in Asia, including two with more than 1 billion people: India and China. The world's greatest mountain range, the Himalayas, is also in Asia. These mountains, which are known as the "Roof of the World," lie between Nepal and China. Mount Everest (29,035 ft/8849 m), the world's highest mountain, is among them.

Mongolia

China

Mongolia

North Korea

South Korea

Japan

PACIFIC OCEAN

South China Sea

Myanmar

Laos

Thailand

Cambodia

Vietnam

Philippines

Brunei

Malaysia

Singapore

Indonesia

Timor-Leste

Philippines

Japan

North Korea

South Korea

China

Laos

Myanmar

Thailand

Vietnam

Cambodia

Timor-Leste

Brunei

Malaysia

Singapore

Indonesia

Flags of Central Asia

Georgia

Cross of St George

Georgian cross, a symbol of Georgia

POPULATION OVER 4.9 MILLION
CAPITAL TBILISI
OFFICIAL LANGUAGE GEORGIAN
NATIONAL ANIMAL LION
NATIONAL FLOWER ROSE
NATIONAL SPORT SOCCER

DID YOU KNOW?
St George is the patron saint of both Georgia and England. Both countries use the cross of St George on a white background on their flags.

Japan

POPULATION OVER 126.4 MILLION
CAPITAL TOKYO
OFFICIAL LANGUAGE JAPANESE
NATIONAL ANIMALS GREEN PHEASANT AND CARP
NATIONAL TREE JAPANESE CHERRY
NATIONAL SPORT SUMO WRESTLING

Sun disc, emblem of Japan

White for purity and honesty

FLAG PROFILE

Adopted: 1999

Called: The *Hi-no-maru* (Japanese for "*Circle of the Sun*")

DID YOU KNOW?
The flag of Japan is one of the easiest flags to recognize. It has a very simple design of a crimson disc against a white background, representing the sun rising into the sky. According to tradition, the sun goddess Amaterasu founded Japan in the 7th century BC. Japan's emperors are thought to be descendants of the sun goddess and a popular name for the country is "Land of the Rising Sun."

Mongolia

Blue for the sky

Red for prosperity

Soyombo national emblem (fire, sun, moon, earth, water, yin-yang symbols)

POPULATION OVER 3 MILLION
CAPITAL ULAANBAATAR
OFFICIAL LANGUAGE MONGOLIAN
NATIONAL ANIMAL PRZEWALSKI'S HORSE
NATIONAL FLOWER
SCABIOSA "BUTTERFLY BLUE"
NATIONAL SPORTS ARCHERY AND
MONGOLIAN WRESTLING

FLAG PROFILE

Adopted: 1992
Called: The State Flag of Mongolia

DID YOU KNOW?

Each part of the emblem on the flag of Mongolia has a meaning. For example, at the top are three tongues of fire, which represent wealth, growth, and success. Below the fire are the symbols of the sun and moon. The triangles represent the points of spears that were used to defeat Mongolia's enemies. See the diagram below for the other symbolism that is present within the emblem.

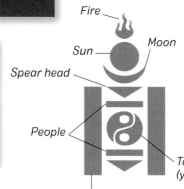

Fire

Sun

Moon

Spear head

People

Taiji symbol (yin-yang)

Fortress walls

The Soyombo symbol is part of a special Mongolian alphabet called the Soyombo script. It was created by a Buddhist leader over 300 years ago and is seen all over the country.

DID YOU KNOW?

The flag of Nepal is made up of two overlapping triangles. They represent the Himalaya mountains, where Nepal is located. It is the only flag in the world that is neither rectangular nor square.

Nepal

Crescent moon, for the cool weather in the Himalayas

POPULATION
OVER 29.3 MILLION
CAPITAL KATHMANDU
OFFICIAL LANGUAGE NEPALI
NATIONAL ANIMAL COW
NATIONAL FLOWER
RHODODENDRON
NATIONAL SPORT
VOLLEYBALL

Crimson for the rhododendron, the national flower

Twelve-pointed sun, for the heat of the lower parts of Nepal

Blue for peace and harmony

FLAG PROFILE

Adopted: 1962
Called: Nepali Flag, Triangle Flag or Chandra ra Surya

Flags of South-East Asia

Four stars for the four stated social classes of people in communist China

Large star for the Communist Party of China

Red for revolution

China

POPULATION OVER 1.3 BILLION

CAPITAL BEIJING

OFFICIAL LANGUAGE
MANDARIN CHINESE

NATIONAL ANIMAL GIANT PANDA

NATIONAL TREE
GINKGO OR MAIDENHAIR TREE

NATIONAL SPORT TABLE TENNIS

DID YOU KNOW?
In 1949, a competition was held to design the flag of China. The government chose a design of five stars on a bright red background. A seamstress was given a few hours to sew just one flag, ready to be flown in Beijing for the first time on October 1, 1949.

FLAG PROFILE

Adopted: 1949

Called: *Five-star Red Flag*

India

POPULATION OVER 1.2 BILLION

CAPITAL NEW DELHI

OFFICIAL LANGUAGES HINDI AND ENGLISH (FOR OFFICIAL PURPOSES)

NATIONAL ANIMALS
BENGAL TIGER AND INDIAN ELEPHANT

NATIONAL TREE
BANYAN TREE

NATIONAL SPORT
FIELD HOCKEY

Saffron orange for courage

Chakra wheel of life (24-spoked wheel)

White for purity and truth

Green for prosperity

FLAG PROFILE

Adopted: 1947

Called: *Tiranga* (Hindi for "*Three Color*")

DID YOU KNOW?
The law says that when the Indian flag is flown in India it must be made from khadi. This is a type of hand-spun cloth of cotton, made in the city of Hubli, south-west India. All of India's flags are made at one factory in Hubli.

Malaysia

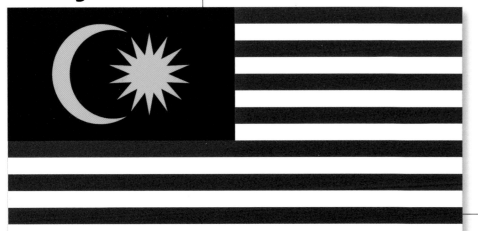

Blue for unity

POPULATION OVER 31.3 MILLION

CAPITAL KUALA LUMPUR

OFFICIAL LANGUAGES MALAY, ENGLISH, CHINESE, AND OTHERS

NATIONAL ANIMAL MALAYAN TIGER

NATIONAL FLOWER HIBISCUS

NATIONAL SPORT SEPAK TAKRAW (SIMILAR TO VOLLEYBALL)

14 stripes for Malaysia's 13 member states plus the district of Kuala Lumpur

DID YOU KNOW?

The flag of Malaysia is based on the flag of the United States. The crescent and star are symbols of Islam, in recognition of the nation's majority Muslim population.

31 August 1957

The flag received its official name in 1997 as part of Malaysia's celebrations of 40 years of independence.

FLAG PROFILE

Adopted: 1963

Called: *Jalur Gemilang* (Malay for *"Stripes of Glory"*

Thailand

POPULATION OVER 68.4 MILLION

CAPITAL BANGKOK

OFFICIAL LANGUAGE THAI

NATIONAL ANIMAL ELEPHANT

NATIONAL TREE GOLDEN RAIN TREE

NATIONAL SPORT KICK BOXING

FLAG PROFILE

Adopted: 1917

Called: *Triarong* (Thai for *"Three Color"*)

Blue, a traditional royal color

White for religion and the purity of Buddhism

Red for the nation and the blood of life

DID YOU KNOW?

The flag of Thailand used to be red with a large white elephant in the center. It was changed to a red, white, and blue flag during World War I, to show support for the United Kingdom, France, Russia, and the United States, whose flags used these colors.

Thailand 1916

White elephants are considered sacred in Thailand and were often given as presents to kings.

Flags of Australia and Oceania

Australia is the largest island in the world and the smallest inhabited continent. To its east are the group of islands that compose New Zealand, and the many scattered island groups within the Pacific Ocean. Together, this vast region is termed "Oceania." The Great Barrier Reef, off the north-east coast of Australia, is a coral reef. It is the largest structure made by living organisms on the planet. Another of Oceania's record-holders is the Mariana Trench, to the north of Papua New Guinea. It is the deepest point in the Earth's crust, where the ocean plunges to a depth of 36,070 ft (10,994 m).

Palau

Palau

Papua New Guinea

Papua New Guinea

Gulf of Carpentaria

Great Barrier Reef

Australia

Great Australian Bight

SOUTHERN OCEAN

Australia

Micronesia

**Marshall
Islands**

Kiribati

Nauru

Micronesia

Marshall Islands

Tuvalu

**Solomon
Islands**

Kiribati

PACIFIC
OCEAN

Samoa

Vanuatu

Fiji

Nauru

**New
Caledonia**

Tonga

Coral
Sea

Solomon Islands

Tuvalu

Samoa

Vanuatu

Fiji

Tasman
Sea

New
Zealand

Tonga

New Zealand

Flags of Australia and Oceania

Australia

Union Jack, for Australia's links with the United Kingdom

Southern Cross constellation, visible in the night sky above Australia

7-pointed Federation Star, for Australia's states and territories

POPULATION OVER 24.5 MILLION
CAPITAL CANBERRA
OFFICIAL LANGUAGE ENGLISH
NATIONAL ANIMAL RED KANGAROO
NATIONAL TREE GOLDEN WATTLE
NATIONAL SPORTS CRICKET AND VARIOUS CODES OF FOOTBALL

FLAG PROFILE

Adopted: officially in 1954, but in use from 1901

Called: *The Australian National Flag*

DID YOU KNOW?
The flag of Australia has two big claims to fame. Firstly, it is the only national flag in the world to fly over an entire continent. Secondly, it was the world's first flag chosen by a public competition—more than 30,000 designs were submitted.

New Zealand

POPULATION OVER 4.7 MILLION
CAPITAL WELLINGTON
OFFICIAL LANGUAGE ENGLISH
NATIONAL ANIMAL KIWI
NATIONAL TREE SILVER FERN
NATIONAL SPORT RUGBY UNION

Union Jack, for New Zealand's links with the United Kingdom

FLAG PROFILE

Adopted: 1902

Called: *The National Flag of New Zealand*

Southern Cross constellation, for New Zealand's location in the South Pacific Ocean

DID YOU KNOW?
The flag of New Zealand could have changed in 2016, when there was a nationwide vote to choose between the existing flag and a new design of a silver fern, in black, white, and blue. Nearly 57% of the people voted to keep the old flag.

The proposed flag featured the silver fern, as seen on the New Zealand dollar coin and the logos of national sports teams.